The Story of Moses

Leena Lane - Gillian Chapman

Moses is hidden in a basket

Moses was born in Egypt. Pharaoh, the king of Egypt, gave a cruel command to drown all the Israelite baby boys in the River Nile.

Moses' mother had a plan to save her little son. She made a basket and coated it with tar. She placed her baby in the basket and hid it among the reeds in the river. The baby's sister, Miriam, watched from behind the reeds.

Pharaoh's daughter, the royal princess, came to the river to bathe. She heard crying from the basket, opened the lid and lifted up the baby.

Miriam stepped out from behind the reeds. 'Shall I fetch an Israelite woman to nurse the baby?' she asked.

So Miriam fetched her own mother! Moses' mother nursed him until he was old enough to go and live in the royal palace as the princess' adopted son.

Exodus 2, verses 1 to 10

✎ Activity:
Can you put baby Moses in the basket?
You can draw the baby and colour him in.

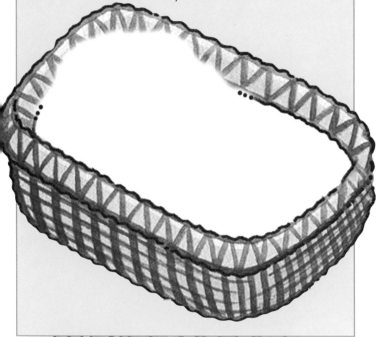

Prayer:
Dear God, thank you for all the people who looked after me when I was a baby and helped me to grow strong.

✎ Activity:
There is only one hidden basket shape like this. Can you find it?

Something to think about:
God protected Moses when he was a tiny baby. God provided people to love him and look after him.

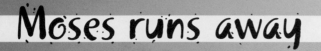

Moses runs away

Activity:

Where did Moses run away to? Can you get there and write the name in the box?

a   b   c

When Moses grew up, he often watched his own Israelite people working as slaves for Pharaoh. He saw how cruelly they were treated.

One day, he saw an Egyptian hitting a slave very hard. Moses was furious. He looked to see if anyone was watching, then he stepped forward and killed the Egyptian. He buried him in the sand.

The next day, Moses saw two slaves fighting and asked why they were hurting each other. One of them said, 'Are you going to kill me now, like you killed that Egyptian yesterday?'

Moses was terrified. Someone had seen him after all. Moses ran away, far from Pharaoh's palace, to a land called Midian.

Exodus 2, verses 11 to 25

Something to think about:

Moses thought no one had seen the bad thing he had done. But they had, and God had seen it too.

Prayer:

Dear God, please help me to tell the truth and not hide the wrong things I do from you.

Welcome to

___ ___ ___ ___ ___ ___ ___

Moses and the burning bush

✎Activity:

Put a circle around the two shoes that belong to Moses.

a
b
c
d
e

Something to think about:

God appeared to Moses in an unexpected place – a burning bush!

Moses lived in Midian for forty years. He married Zipporah and had a son.

Moses looked after Zipporah's father's sheep and goats, leading them across the desert places and mountains to find grass and water.

One day, when Moses was looking after the sheep at Horeb, the mountain of God, he saw an amazing sight.

There was a burning bush in front of him, which did not burn up.

God called to Moses from within the bush: 'Moses! Moses!'

Moses stepped closer to the bush.

'Take off your sandals,' said God. 'You are standing on holy ground.' At once, Moses covered his eyes.

'I am the God of your father, the God of Abraham, the God of Isaac and the God of Jacob,' said God. 'I have seen my people suffering. I am sending you to Pharaoh to bring my people out of Egypt.'

Exodus 3, verses 1 to 22

Activity:
Colour in this picture of Moses and the burning bush.

Prayer:
Dear God, help me to be ready to listen to you wherever I am.

'I can't do it!'

God told Moses to go to Pharaoh and ask him to let the Israelite slaves go free. God told Moses to tell the Israelites that he would be their leader.

But Moses was worried. 'What if no one listens to me?' he said.

'Look at the staff in your hand,' said God. 'Throw it to the ground.'

At once the staff became a snake!

When Moses took the snake by the tail, it turned back into a staff.

'But I am not very good at speaking,' said Moses.

'I will help you,' said God.

'But I can't do it!' said Moses. 'Please send someone else!'

God became angry with Moses.

'Your brother, Aaron, can help you. I will help you both,' said God.

Exodus 3, verses 7 to 9;
Exodus 4, verses 1 to 17

Activity:

Can you draw a pattern on the snake and colour it in?

Something to think about:
Moses thought he wasn't clever enough to do what God wanted. But God wouldn't take no for an answer!

Prayer:
Dear God, help me to be willing to do the things you ask me. Help me this week to...

Activity:
Can you find five snakes in the word search?

```
Q T D I S G C Z M Y A
W A P Y T H O N R S P
A O R D N R B F A G L
R M W O U E R S T R P
B A I U J C A D T A G
Y R T B R S P F L S A
F A D D E R O Y E S C
```

Moses goes to see Pharaoh

Moses and his brother Aaron went to see Pharaoh.

'God says, let my people go!' they said boldly.

But Pharaoh replied, 'Who is your God? I do not know him. I shall not let the people go.'

Pharaoh became even more cruel to the Israelite slaves. They made bricks from straw and mud. Now Pharaoh made them find their own straw. This made them work very slowly.

'You are all very lazy!' said Pharaoh.

The Israelite men in charge of the slaves became angry with Moses and Aaron. 'You have just made things worse for us all!' they shouted.

But Moses and Aaron told them what God had said. God promised to set them free. Moses and Aaron believed it, even though the other Israelites would not listen.

Exodus 5, verses 1 to 23

Prayer:

Dear God, thank you that you can see the big picture and your plans for my life. Help me to trust you more.

Something to think about:

Things did not go quite as Moses planned. He obeyed God, but for a time things seemed to get worse!

Activity:

Draw a line to connect each detail to the right spot in the picture.

Activity:

Draw a circle around the four symbols that are exactly the same as symbols on the far left.

The plagues of Egypt

Pharaoh would not listen to the cry of the Israelites. Moses and Aaron tried to persuade him to let the people go. They even performed miracles.

Then God told Moses to stretch out his staff over the River Nile. The water turned to blood! The Egyptians were unable to drink the water any more or bathe in it.

Next, God sent a plague of frogs. Frogs hopped into everyone's house and bed, even into the royal palace.

Then came a plague of gnats, then flies, which filled the Egyptians' houses.

Another plague fell upon the land. This time all the cows and sheep died. Then all the Egyptians were covered in boils and their skin became terribly sore. Still Pharaoh wouldn't budge.

A plague of hailstones hit the land, then locusts came and devoured the crops. Darkness fell upon the land and no one could see.

But the final plague was the most terrible of all. Moses warned Pharaoh that all the firstborn children of Egypt would die in a night.

Exodus 7 to 11

Something to think about:

Why do you think Pharaoh would not let the Israelite people go?

Prayer:

Dear God, thank you that you are very powerful and that you are on my side in times of trouble.

What was the name of the river that turned to blood?

How many plagues were there all together?

✎ Activity:

Can you number these six plagues in the right order?

The Passover meal

God told Moses to tell all the Israelites to get ready. They must each take a lamb, kill it, and put some of the lamb's blood on the doorposts of the house. They must then roast the lamb over a fire and eat the meat, with bitter herbs and bread made without yeast. This was to be called the Passover.

That night, death came to Egypt. All the firstborn sons and animals of the Egyptians died.

Even Pharaoh's son died. There was terrible wailing in the land.

Death passed over all the homes of the Israelites but not one was harmed. God saved them all.

Pharaoh called Moses and Aaron. 'Go!' he said. 'Leave Egypt! Take your animals and go, as you asked.'

The final terrible plague made Pharaoh change his mind. He let the people go.

Exodus 12, verses 1 to 32

✎ Activity:

There are eight things that are missing from this
picture. Can you find all the changes?
Draw an arrow from each number to a change.

 1

 2

 3

 4

 5

 6

7

 8

Something to think about:

God told his people to
remember the Passover
for ever.

Can you think of a
way in which your church
celebrates how God
saved his people?

Prayer:

Dear God, you kept the
Israelites safe during the
Passover because they were
your special people. Thank
you that I am special to you
too.

Crossing the Red Sea

God led the Israelites out of Egypt. He went ahead of them in a pillar of cloud by day, and a pillar of fire at night. God led them to the Red Sea.

Pharaoh, meanwhile, suddenly changed his mind about letting the Israelites go! He sent soldiers on horses and in chariots to chase after them.

Moses told his people not to be afraid, even though Pharaoh's troops were coming nearer and nearer!

Moses stretched his staff over the water of the Red Sea. The water parted! The Israelites passed through the Red Sea on dry land and reached the other side.

Pharaoh's soldiers tried to follow, but Moses raised his staff over the water again and the sea came crashing down. All the Egyptians were drowned.

When the Israelites saw how powerful God was, they put their trust in him and believed what Moses said.

Exodus 14, verses 1 to 31

Something to think about:

The Israelites thought they were trapped, but God saved them in an amazing way!

Prayer:

Lord, you can do amazing things! Please help me when I face danger or scary situations like...

✎ Activity:

Can you find these faces in the crowd? Put a number in each box to identify each face. Which face is not in the crowd?

Manna and quail

'**W**here's the food?' grumbled the Israelites.

God had guided them across the Red Sea to safety on the other side, away from Egypt and Pharaoh at last. But now the Israelites were grumbling. And their stomachs were rumbling...

'I will send bread from heaven for you,' said God to Moses.

'The people must go out and gather enough for one day at a time. On the sixth day of the week, they must bring in twice as much as on the other days, so that they can rest on the seventh day.'

That evening, quail flew over the camp and the people caught them.

In the morning, dew covered the ground. When it had gone, there were flakes of white manna on the ground. It was the bread from heaven which God had sent. It tasted like wafers made with honey.

God had provided for all their needs once again.

Exodus 16, verses 1 to 36

Something to think about:

Why do you think that God told the people to collect enough food for one day at a time?

✎ Activity:

What is missing from this picture?

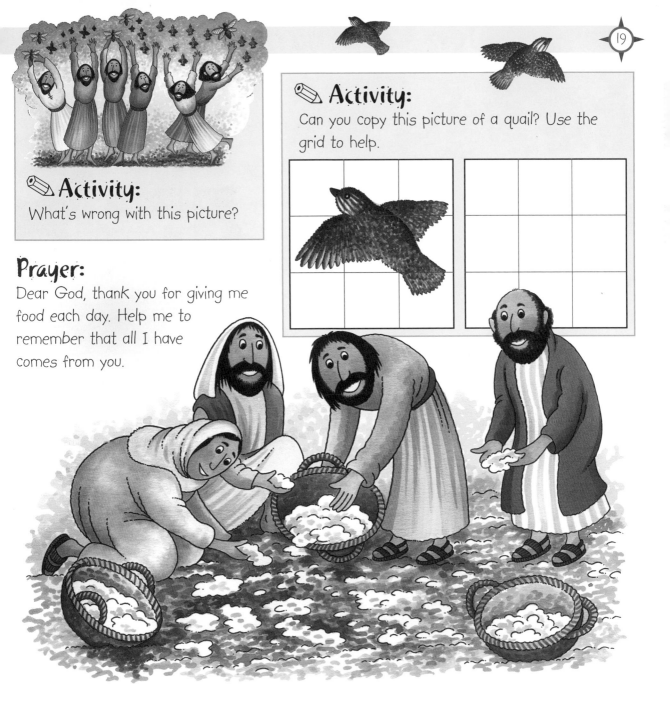

✎ Activity:

What's wrong with this picture?

✎ Activity:

Can you copy this picture of a quail? Use the grid to help.

Prayer:

Dear God, thank you for giving me food each day. Help me to remember that all I have comes from you.

The Ten Commandments

Moses went up Mount Sinai to talk to God.

'You know what I have done for you,' said God. 'I have carried you on eagle's wings and brought you to myself. Obey me and my commandments and I will make Israel into a great nation, my most special nation in the whole earth. I will make a covenant with you.'

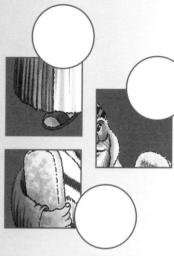

1	2
3	4
5	6
7	8

✏️ Activity:

To re-create this picture the squares have to be put in the correct place, Can you put the correct position number in each circle?

20

God gave Moses laws called the Ten Commandments:

'I am the Lord your God. Have no other gods besides me.

Do not make statues or anything else to worship.

Do not use my name carelessly.

Remember to keep the seventh day holy.

Do not work on this day.

Respect your father and mother.

Do not murder anyone.

Do not be unfaithful to your wife or husband.

Do not steal.

Do not tell lies about anyone.

Do not look greedily at things other people have got.'

There was thunder and lightning and a trumpet blast. The laws were written on stone tablets.

Exodus 19 to 20

Prayer:

Dear God, help me to remember that you are very holy. Help me to live in a way which pleases you.

Activity:

What is the number of the day that we keep holy?

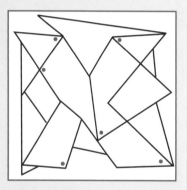

Activity:

God gave Moses ten laws. Colour in the shapes with a red dot to see how the Romans wrote ten.

Something to think about:

Think about the Ten Commandments which God gave to Moses. Which ones do you find hard to keep?

The Promised Land

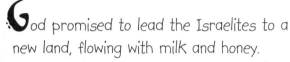

God promised to lead the Israelites to a new land, flowing with milk and honey.

It took many years to reach the land which God had promised. On the way there, God spoke to Moses many times. He told Moses to build the tabernacle – a holy place where people would worship God. Aaron was made a high priest. Special objects were made for the tabernacle: a golden lampstand, and the ark of the Covenant. This was a sacred box which contained the stone tablets with the laws God gave to Moses on Mount Sinai.

When Moses was a very old man, God took him to the top of a mountain. From there he could see a new land in the distance. It was the promised land!

But Moses never set foot there. He died. God chose Joshua to continue the journey.

Deuteronomy 34 and Joshua 1

Something to think about:

Do you remember how Moses had been afraid to lead the people of Israel when God first asked him? Think of ways in which God helped him.

Activity:
Can you find your way to the promised land?

Prayer:
Dear God, please help me to trust you when I have something difficult to do. I know that you are always able to help me.

Published in the UK by
The Bible Reading Fellowship
First Floor, Elsfield Hall, 15-17 Elsfield Way, Oxford OX2 8FG
ISBN 1 84101 452 4

First edition 2005
Copyright © 2005 AD Publishing Services Ltd
1 Churchgates, The Wilderness, Berkhamsted, Herts HP4 2UB
Text copyright © 2005 AD Publishing Services Ltd, Leena Lane
Illustrations copyright © 2005 Gillian Chapman

Editorial Director Annette Reynolds
Art Director Gerald Rogers
Pre-production Krystyna Hewitt
Production John Laister

British Library Cataloguing in Publication Data.
A catalogue record for this book is available from the British Library.

Printed and bound in Singapore